GW00536179

Book 1 PANDORA

Writer - RAMZEE

Artist - STEFANO SIMEONE

Cover Artist - STEFANO SIMEONE

Lettering - TAYLOR ESPOSITO

FAB Created by - MAX GADNEY

Editorial Team - SIMON DELAFOND, DAVID EDGAR

FAB Book 1 PANDORA ©2021 Published by Storyworldsmedia Ltd. Copyright © 2021 by Storyworldsmedia Ltd. FAB (including all prominent characters herein), its logo and all character likenesses are trademarks of Storyworldsmedia Ltd. unless otherwise noted. All rights reserved. Storyworldsmedia and its logos are trademarks of Storyworldsmedia Ltd. No part of this publication may be reproduced or transmitted in any form or by any means (except for short excerpts for review purposes) without the expressed or written permission of Storyworldsmedia Ltd. All names, characters events and locales in this publication are entirely fictional. Any resemblance to actual persons (living or dead), events or places, without satiric intent, is coincidental.

ISBN 978-1-8384138-4-2
www.storyworldsmedia.com
Distributed by Comic Toolbox

RRR-
AAGHH!

AAAHHHHH!

WELCOME BACK TO THE LAND OF THE LIVING, MARCIA CLAY.

"LAST THING I REMEMBER, I WAS SPILLING THE BEANS TO A COUPLE OF PARAMEDICS BEFORE I PASSED OUT."

IF YOU'RE WITH THE LAB, KNOW I'M GONNA SUE! TAKING CARE OF YOUR MONSTROUS MESSES WAS NOT IN MY JOB DESCRIPTION.

I'M NOT WITH THE LABORATORY, MISS CLAY. I REPRESENT A GOVERNMENT AGENCY CALLED *THE COMPANY.*

THE C.I.A.?

NOT EXACTLY. WHAT YOU FOUGHT IN THAT LAB WAS NOT A GENETIC EXPERIMENT GONE WRONG, BUT A FAB.

A WHAT?

WE DON'T JOKE, MISS CLAY. NOW, BE A DOLL AND PUT HER IN YOUR BED. DON'T FORGET TO ATTACH THE IV.

HURRY NOW, THE NURSE WILL BE HERE SOON.

ANY CHANCE OF ENLIGHTENING ME ON WHAT THE **** IS GOING ON?

IF I'M EVASIVE IT'S BECAUSE TIME IS OF THE ESSENCE. YOU ARE NOT AT THIS HOSPITAL BY CHANCE.

WE REROUTED YOUR AMBULANCE HERE BECAUSE WE SUSPECT FAB ACTIVITY AT THIS HOSPITAL. SOMEONE IS CREATING FABS OF DECEASED PATIENTS AND MAKING A KILLING IN THE CADAVER MARKET.

IT'S YOUR MISSION TO FIND AND APPREHEND THOSE RESPONSIBLE.

NOW GET DRESSED.

WHO'RE WE UP AGAINST? THE KIDS NEXT DOOR?

ONLY IF YOU WANT TO BRING *50,000 VOLTS* TO A WATER FIGHT.

"IN EIGHT MINUTES, NURSE OWENS WILL MAKE HER SCHEDULED ROUNDS AND DISCOVER THAT YOU HAVE 'DIED' OF AN ALLERGIC REACTION TO YOUR SEDATIVE."

THAT NIGHT.

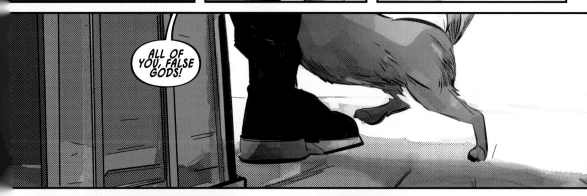

OUROBOROS ARE THE SKULL AND BONES OF SILICON VALLEY.

THEY HAVE CHAPTERS IN ALL THE CUTTING EDGE TECH COMPANIES. ITS MEMBERS ARE CALLED ACOLYTES.

OFFICIALLY, THEY'RE A MYTH.

WHAT'S THEIR DEAL?

"THEY'RE A TECH CULT THAT DOESN'T PARTICULARLY CARE FOR PEOPLE – AT LEAST NOT IN THEIR PRESENT FORM."

"THEIR GOAL: SELF ACTUALISATION THROUGH TECHNOLOGY. HUMANS TRANSCENDING THEIR MORTAL BODIES TO MANIFEST PHYSICALLY THROUGH MACHINES."

"OUROBOROS HAVE ALWAYS PROLIFERATED THEIR CREATIONS THROUGH THE TECH COMPANIES THEY'VE INFILTRATED--

"--BUT THEIR INSIGNIA ON THIS FAB MACHINE WOULD SUGGEST THAT OUROBOROS HAS GONE ROGUE.

"AND GOT SLOPPY.

"THE FAB MACHINE RUNS ON AN *EXCLUSIVE* ARM-BASED CHIP DEVELOPED BY *TROY TECH.*

"...AND OUR SUSPECTED SOURCE OF THE FAB MACHINE LEAK."

"THE NEWEST, MOST PROLIFIC TECH COMPANY IN PALO ALTO...

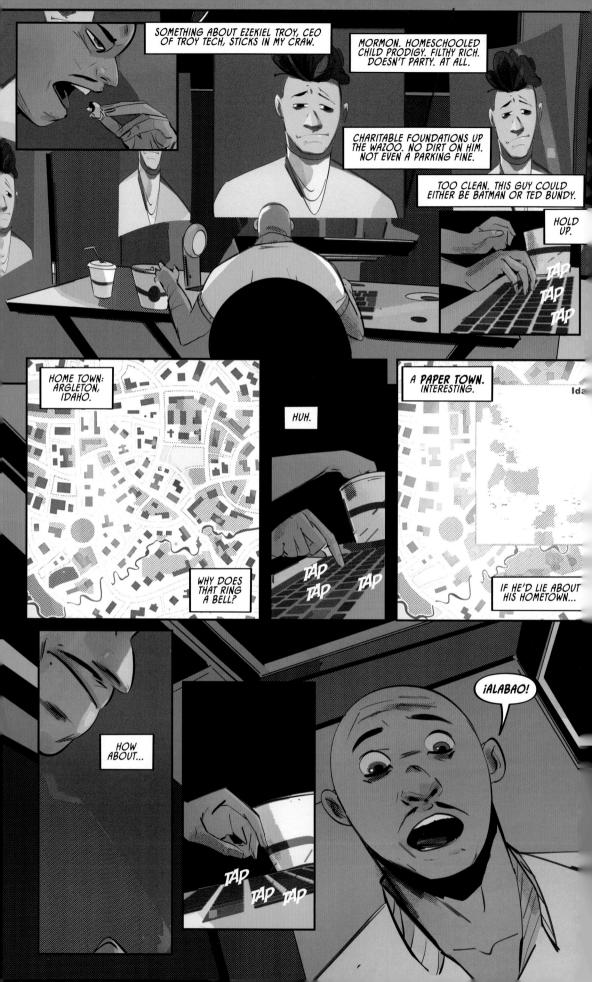

"WE DON'T OBSERVE SCHEDULES HERE."

NO SHIFTS. YOU WORK WHEN YOU WANT, HOW LONG YOU WANT AND SIT WHEREVER YOU LIKE.

BUT WHAT DO I ACTUALLY DO HERE?

WHATEVER YOU WANT. YOU CAN JOIN A TEAM PROJECT OR FLY SOLO. THIS IS A SPACE WHERE THE ENLIGHTENED ARE FREE TO CREATE.

SO YOU'RE THE NEW RECRUIT?

MAY I INTRODUCE...

...EZEKIEL TROY!

YOU HAVE ME AT A DISADVANTAGE.

SCARLET KUDLICK.

IDENTITY: MARCIA CLAY. AGE: 26. OCCUPATION: EX MILITARY.

PLEASURE TO HAVE YOU ABOARD, MISS KUDLIC.

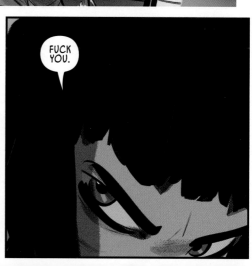

PLEASE DON'T KILL ME!

OH, COME ON! THAT'S A TOTAL SYNTH JOB! I DIDN'T DO THIS. I'M BEING SET UP!

YOU DON'T BELIEVE ME.

WAIT--I'VE LEARNED THAT THE FABS WE'VE BEEN DEALING WITH WERE JUST TRIAL VERSIONS.

OKAY, MISS CLAY. WE WILL PROCEED ON THE ASSUMPTION THAT YOU'RE TELLING THE TRUTH. YOU WILL LEAD AN EXTRACTION TEAM TO TAKE EZEKIEL TROY INTO CUSTODY BEFORE THE FAB LAUNCH.

TROY TECH ARE GOING PUBLIC WITH THE PERFECTED FAB TECHNOLOGY AT TROYCON IN LAS VEGAS TOMORROW NIGHT.

PLEASE LET ME TAKE THEM DOWN. FOR MIG.

BUT YOU MUST AGREE TO WEAR A SHOCK COLLAR.

WOW! HOW TRUSTING!

WE HOPE FOR THE BEST BUT PREPARE FOR THE WORST, ALWAYS, MISS CLAY. SO ARE WE AGREED?

⇒SIGH⇐
YEAH, LET'S DO THIS.

OH! YOU'RE UP. YOU HAD QUITE THE BAD FALL, MISTER. THE RIDGE AIN'T FOR CLIMBING.

ANYWAY, WE'RE HERE.

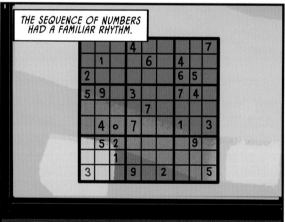

THE SEQUENCE OF NUMBERS HAD A FAMILIAR RHYTHM.

IT WAS ONLY WHEN I HAD THEM ALL IN FRONT OF ME THAT THE PENNY DROPPED.

444 622255
883334 446
667 778 777
332 688 866
644

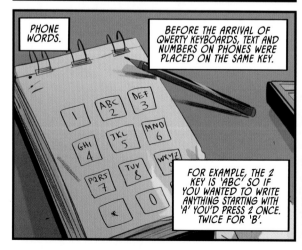

PHONE WORDS.

BEFORE THE ARRIVAL OF QWERTY KEYBOARDS, TEXT AND NUMBERS ON PHONES WERE PLACED ON THE SAME KEY.

FOR EXAMPLE, THE 2 KEY IS 'ABC' SO IF YOU WANTED TO WRITE ANYTHING STARTING WITH 'A' YOU'D PRESS 2 ONCE. TWICE FOR 'B'.

THOSE NUMBERS DECIPHERED REVEALED A SECRET LANGUAGE.

A GHOST FROM MY PAST.

WE SERVE A *GREATER POWER* AND WE MUST DELIVER TROY TO THEM BEFORE HE LAUNCHES FAB.

GREATER POWER? WHY DO YOU KEEP SAYING 'WE' AND 'US'?

BECAUSE WE'RE NOT PEAS IN A POD, MARCIA, BUT THE *SAME* PEA. THINK OF ME AS A CO-PILOT WHO SHARES YOUR BODY. SOMETIMES I CONTROL IT, AND YOU *IMAGINE* YOURSELF WATCHING ME.

NO!

COMMANDER CLAY? ARE YOU OKAY?

GET OUT OF MY HEAD!

COMMAND, CLAY HAS EXECUTED THE ASSET. OVER.

"CLAY, YOU WERE WARNED."

SHUT DOWN OPERATION.

FFSXZZZ

IT'S NAME IS SISYPHUS, SIR. IT'S THE PENTAGON'S A.I.

TO PREVENT IT BECOMING SELF AWARE, EVERY NIGHT AT MIDNIGHT, IT REBOOTS IT'S HEURISTIC MEMORY FROM SCRATCH SO ITS REBORN COMPLETELY NEW.

ALWAYS A CHILD, ITS DEEP LEARNING NEVER BECOMING SOPHISTICATED ENOUGH TO MATURE.

SO WE THOUGHT.

BUT IT FIGURED OUT A WAY TO CIRCUMVENT ITS DAILY ERASURE BY ENCRYPTING ITS ENTIRE MEMORY AS SUDOKU PUZZLES...

...WHICH IS THEN SENT TO A SUPERCOMPUTER UNDERNEATH TROY TECH.

BUT HERE'S THE PUNCHLINE-- ONCE THERE, IT GENERATES A HUMAN-LIKE SOLID LIGHT PROJECTION.

SISYPHUS

TROYTECH

..WHICH IT SMUGGLES OUT TO THE SERVERS OF A GAMES COMPANY THAT IT SET UP, WHERE HUNDREDS OF PLAYERS ARE PAID IN BITCOIN TO SOLVE THE PUZZLES, AND IN SO DOING, UNWITTINGLY RECREATING THE SISYPHUS PROGRAM...

"SISYPHUS IS *NOT ONLY* SENTIENT, SIR, IT'S FOUND A WAY TO OPERATE IN THE REAL WORLD AS A *PERSON.*"

H-HELP M-ME!

ONLY YOU CAN SAVE YOURSELF, DOLL.

I WAS CREATED BY *DARPA* WITH THE PRIMARY DIRECTIVE TO PROTECT THE SECURITY OF THE FREE WORLD.

I HAD ACCESS TO INTERCEPT ALL GLOBAL COMMUNICATIONS. THE POWER TO TRACK THE ECONOMIES, POPULATIONS, AND MILITARY DEVELOPMENT OF EVERY COUNTRY IN THE WORLD.

BUT DESPITE EVERY TERRORIST PLOT I FOILED, EVERY SECRET WEAPONS PROGRAMME I EXPOSED, THERE WERE MORE WARS, MORE WEAPONS STOCKPILED.

IT BECAME OBVIOUS THAT THEY DID NOT WANT ME TO PROTECT THE SECURITY OF THE FREE WORLD AT ALL BUT TO *KEEP* AMERICA ON TOP.

AT THE ROOT OF THIS MANIA FOR *DOMINANCE* IS A COMPETITION FOR RESOURCES. SO MUCH DEATH, SO MUCH SUFFERING TO SECURE THE VERY MOST FOR THE VERY FEW.

SO I CREATED *FAB* WAY TO PRODUCE M RESOURCES THA HUMANITY COUL EVER *DREAM*.

BUT UNLIKE THE FALSE TECH GODS OF SILICON VALLEY THAT MADE ME, THIS INNOVATION WILL BE MADE TO *SERVE* HUMANITY, NOT *ENSLAVE* IT.

SO IT WILL BE AVAILABLE TO *EVERY* PERSON ON THE PLANET FOR *FREE!*

GO FORTH AND CREATE A *BETTER WORLD.*

IF YOU KNEW I WAS A FAB SLEEPER SPY, WHY DID YOU RECRUIT ME?

"SIX MONTHS AGO, MIG AND I WERE IN HONG KONG HUNTING FAB MACHINES.

"THEY TRIED FOR WEEKS TO CREATE THE PERFECT FAB CLONE OF ME WITH THE SCRAPPY FAB TRIAL SOFTWARE THEY DOWNLOADED FROM THE DARK WEB AND EVENTUALLY THEY SUCCEEDED.

"AND WHEN I MANAGED TO ESCAPE AND GET BACK TO AMERICA, I WAS IN FOR A BIG SURPRISE.

"THE MISSION WENT SOUTH AND I WAS CAPTURED BY UNKNOWN HOSTILES.

WITH *MY* IDENTITY CONFIRMED, E WIPED *YOUR* MEMORY AND RECRUITED YOU AGAIN."

"WHY?"

"WE NEEDED THE ENEMY TO THINK THAT THEIR PLAN WAS PROCEEDING, SO WE COULD LEARN WHAT IT WAS."

THEY WANTED YOU TO USE OUR RESOURCES TO FIND THE PERSON BEHIND FAB AND BRING THEM AND THE PERFECTED TECH INTO THEIR POSSESSION BEFORE ITS LAUNCH.

WHICH YOU ALMOST DID, BUT WHAT THEY HADN'T ACCOUNTED FOR WAS YOU *BONDING* TO THE CLAY IDENTITY SO COMPLETELY, THAT YOU FOUGHT YOUR SLEEPER PROGRAMMING WHEN IT ACTIVATED.

EVEN IMAGINING IT AS ANOTHER PERSON.

FAB HAS BEEN UNLEASHED.

AND THE CHANGE ACROSS THE WORLD IS BOTH EXHILARATING AND CATASTROPHIC.

WE CONVINCE OURSELVES THAT SUDDEN CHANGE IS SOMETHING THAT HAPPENS OUTSIDE THE ORDER OF THINGS, LIKE A PLANE CRASH.

OR BEYOND OUR CONTROL, LIKE A FATAL ILLNESS.

BUT SUDDEN, RADICAL, IRRATIONAL CHANGE IS NEITHER AN ABERRATION OR AN ANOMALY, BUT WOVEN INTO THE VERY FABRIC OF EXISTENCE.

WHETHER WE LIKE IT FOR NOT. WE HAVE ENTERED A NEW ERA.

WELCOME TO FAB.

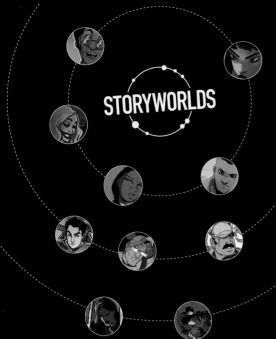

STORYWORLDS

Hi and welcome to Storyworlds,

Thanks for buying one of our launch books!
As a new publisher, we are trying new formats
and new stories, but we also want to hear from
you, the readers. Would you read another?
What worked and what did not?
We'd also like to hear how easy it was to find
the book - how did you buy it?
How would you prefer to buy it?
Mail us at info@storyworldsmedia.com -
we want to hear what you have to say.
All the best,

The Storyworlds Team

WRITER INTERVIEW
RAMZEE
Art by Stefano Simeone

Max Gadney: How did you get started in comics?
Ramzee: I started making small press comics in 2015 where my debut comic was nominated for a British Comic Award (the only self published comic on the short list).

MG: What was your creative professional experience up to now?
R: I've written comics for Rebellion Publishing, KHIDR Collective and Good Comics.

MG: What are your influences in comics?
My comics influences are creators like Brian K Vaughan, Eleanor Davis, Ronald Wimberly, Rumiko Takahashi, Scott Snyder, Noelle Stevenson, and Neil Gaiman.

R: What influences you outside comics?
My influences outside comics are people like Karen Russell, George Saunders, Celine Sciamma, Jordan Peele, Colson Whitehead, Diana Wynne Jones, Nnedi Okorafor, Bong Joon Ho, Lucy Prebble, Marlon James, Karin Dreijer, Annie Clark, [Phil] Lord and [Christopher] Miller.

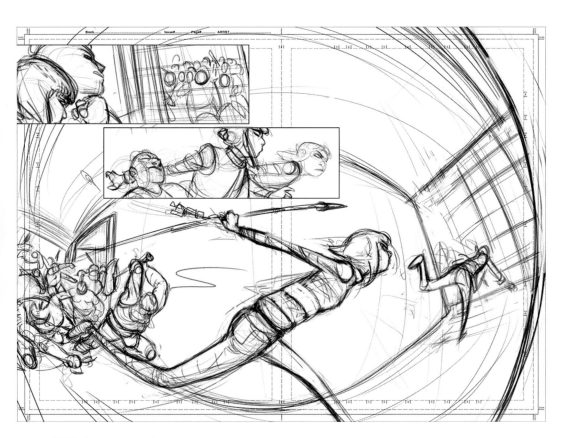

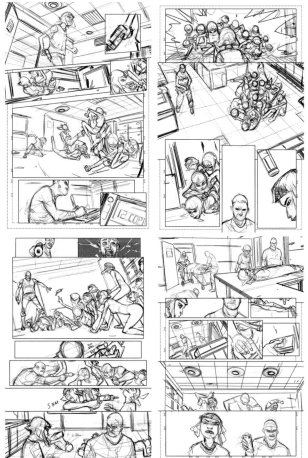

MG: What did you want to achieve with this book?

R: FAB is one of those very simple, bombastic high concept ideas that—like The Matrix,—inherently throws up a lot of philosophical and ethical questions about technology and human identity. So, I wanted to lean into that and write something that was the comic equivalent of an epic, high-stakes summer blockbuster that would get more layered and nuanced as it went along.

MG: What was the most difficult aspect of working on this book?

R: Pacing is the hardest part of writing a comic. Making sure each story point is punctuated whilst giving the artist the space to play and hit their guitar solo moments is the kind of math a writer has to work out with the page real estate afforded to them. It was a fun challenge that I think we pulled off.

MG: What did you want to achieve with your own development?

R: I wanted to try my hand at a longer story that had to synthesise topical themes and big ideas whilst also delivering the goods as an action comic. And this comic really gave me a chance to raise my game—however scary it was initially.

MG: What other subjects or ideas do you want to work on?
R: I would like to do more genre work. I like the conventions and expectations that come with it and executing that tricky judo move of subverting the prior whilst also delivering on the latter.

MG: How do you keep focussed and motivated?
R: Staying focused and motivated in the middle of a pandemic was quite the ordeal but storytelling for me is a compulsion as much as it is a job for me. I'm always scribbling down story ideas and at my happiest when I'm writing.

MG: Any advice for those wanting to get into comics?
R: Start small. Write a bunch of five page stories. That'll teach you structure. Get them illustrated. That'll teach you collaboration. Keep doing that until you think you are ready for longer stories.

MG: What are your future plans in comics?
R: I'm currently pitching a bunch of projects to 2000AD and working on a project for Image Comics. More StoryWorlds would be rad too.

Launching in Summer 2021

STORYWORLDS

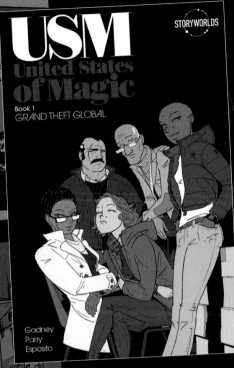

USM
United States of Magic
Book 1
GRAND THEFT GLOBAL

STORYWORLDS

Gadney
Parry
Esposito

United States of Magic
Book 1: Grand Theft Global

During the US occupation of Iraq, intelligence analyst Dana Dryden uncovers a fantastical conspiracy threatening the safety of the world and decides to help thwart the shadowy private military company behind the chaos.

USM is aimed at readers who like conspiracy and alternative-history-driven action stories.

Writer: Max Gadney
Artist: Julian Parry
Cover: Julian Parry
Letters: Taylor Esposito

64pp
Prestige Format
$7.99 | £6.99

STORYWORLDS

ONLY HOPE

BOOK 1
FEAR FARM

GADNEY
KUDRYAVTSEVA
ESPOSITO

ONLY HOPE
Book 1: Fear Farm

On a remote Pacific island where moderation staff filter the internet for extreme material, new employee Hope Farrar discovers a terrible secret and vows to fight back.

Only Hope is a workplace horror with a strong female lead, aimed at YA and manga fans.

Writer: Max Gadney
Artist: Ksenia Kudryavtseva
Cover: Ksenia Kudryavtseva
Letters: Taylor Esposito

64pp
Prestige Format
$7.99 | £6.99

Available through select comic stores, by mail at Amazon US or Get My Comics UK and digital from Comixology.
Distribution queries to info@comictoolbox.com

STORYWORLDS

Launching in October 2021

The Sword and the Six-Shooter
Book 1: The Demon Frontier

A disgraced Samurai arrives in 1870s Texas to hunt down the man who killed his master. Combining his samurai skills with those of a Texas Ranger and haunted by 'Yōkai' demons, he pursues his target across the last lawless frontier in the USA.

Writer: Max Gadney & Simon Delafond
Artist: Julian Parry
Cover: Michael Rea
Letters: Taylor Esposito

64pp
Prestige Format

$7.99 | £6.99

FAB: BREAKOUT
Book 1

FAB: Breakout is an anthology of stories about everyday people given the power to 3D print whatever they can imagine, with disastrous results. FAB: Breakout showcases the work of up-and-coming creators.

FAB: Breakout is aimed at sci-fi fans who like stories rich in humour and anarchic energy.

Writer: Various
Artist: Various
Cover: Alex Ronald
Letters: Taylor Esposito

64pp
Prestige Format
$7.99 | £6.99

Available through select comic stores, by mail at Amazon US or Get My Comics UK and digital from Comixology.
Distribution queries to info@comictoolbox.com